Who Greased the Shoelaces?

Who Greased the Shoelaces?

Lois Simmie
Illustrations by Anne Simmie

(Stoddart)

First published in 1989 by
Stoddart Publishing Co. Limited
34 Lesmill Road
Toronto, Canada
M3B 2T6

CANADIAN CATALOGUING IN PUBLICATION DATA

Simmie, Lois, 1932-
   Who greased the shoelaces?

Poems.
ISBN 0-7737-2365-X (hardcover)   ISBN 7737-5311-7 (pbk)

1. Children's poetry, Canadian (English).*
I. Simmie, Anne, 1956-   . II. Title.

PS8587.I314 1989   jC811'.54   C89-094482-2
PR9199.3.S5185 1989

Cover Design: Linda Gustafson
Cover Illustration: Anne Simmie

Printed in the United States of America

For Justin, Melissa, Odette and Daniel
and for their
great-grandma, Margaret Binns

Contents

Part One: Dinosaurs and Others

Part Two: Who Greased the Shoelaces?

Part One

Dinosaurs and Others

DORIS BRONTOSAURUS

Doris Brontosaurus lived in a forest
Back in the time before history;
Doris Brontosaurus sang in a chorus,
What Doris B. sang is a mystery.

ANKYLOSAURUS

An awesome sight in studs and spikes
And other fancy junk;
Ankylosaurus had to be
A prehistoric punk.

HANDY INSECT IDENTIFICATION GUIDE

If it's camped on your lawn with a tiny wee fire,
It's a tent caterpillar you see;
If it carries a chain saw and saws up your house,
It's a carpenter ant on a spree;
If it smartly salutes you while marching along,
It's an army worm — private, no doubt;
If it sits by your window and howls at the moon,
It's a wolf spider. Let it out.

FUSSY

Little Miss Muffet sat on a tuffet
Eating her curds and whey;
Along came a spider
And sat down beside her
And said, "Yecchhh!!!
I thought you were eating
Cheerios."

MATINEE

I saw a mouse in the lineup today
Going to the matinee;
He was waiting with a cricket
Who didn't have a ticket.
They sat up in the balcony,
Right in front, so they could see.

TYRANNOSAURUS REX

It must be going to rain,
Thought Tyrannosaurus Rex,
Glolloping along through the clover;
When no rain fell on his head
Tyrannosaurus said,
"Oh, it's only Pterodactyl passing over."

ELASMOSAURUS

Elasmosaurus swam with ease
Humungous prehistoric seas;
He didn't have problems with cramps in the toes,
He didn't get water, just air, in his nose;
Elasmosaurus sure could swim,
But so could I, if I were him.

GOING FOR THE MAIL

The spotted horse and the paisley snail
Went out one morning to get the mail;
The box was too high for the snail to see
So she called to the horse, "Is there any for me?"

"There's *The Snail Gazette* and *Snail Trails,*
There's a card from your cousin Bea;
She's been on the road for a month or so
And she's only got to the second tree.

"Here's *The Racing News* and *The Healthy Horse*
And a thing for a horseshoe sale;
There's a card from my aunt in Arabia...
Uncle Harry's back in jail."

The spotted horse and the paisley snail
Went out one morning to get the mail;
The next day too, and the one after that,
And every day except Sun. and Sat.

STEGOSAURUS

A peaceable fellow was Stegosaurus,
You might even call him lazy,
Lunching and munching and mooching around
Like a wandering ten-ton daisy.

TRICERATOPS

Triceratops don't care a lot
For any other creatures;
Triceratops just stare a lot,
And sneer a lot, and glare a lot,
And snort into the air a lot;
Triceratops can't *bear* a lot
Of other creatures' features.

LYLE

A parrot out in Stanley Park was looking sad and gloomy; his feathers were all moulting and his eyes were shut up tight. "Polly want a cracker?" asked some people by his cage, but he didn't move and you could see he had no appetite.

So the people went away to feed the monkeys and the ducks, and I stood and watched that parrot for a while. Imagine my surprise when he opened up his eyes and clear as day he said, "My name is Lyle.

"I am so sick to death of people, all so stupid and so jolly, who just assume — they never ask — a parrot's name is Polly. 'Polly want a cracker?' is all they ever say; never, 'How about a steak, Lyle? An oyster? Or soufflé?'

"Do they seek out my opinion on the economic crisis? Or ask about my state of melancholy? Do they speak to me in Latin? Or ask what twice times twice is? Do they ever? No, they all shout, 'Pretty Polly!'

"'What's the matter, Pretty Polly? Has the cat got your tongue?'
And they shove those awful crackers in my face; I've been
perching on this perch for a hundred years or more and I'm
tired of your stupid human race.

"MY NAME IS LYLE!" He screeched it out. "MY *#!*#! NAME'S
NOT POLLY! I DON'T WANT A *##!*! CRACKER, DO YOU
HEAR!!!"

He shut his beak and closed his eyes behind their leathery
lids, and now I guess I know why parrots swear.

PENTACERATOPS

Pentaceratops was splendid
And wonderfully gorgeous,
An elegant beast to behold;
He looked like a big piece of jewelry
God just forgot to spray gold.

JEREMIAH

A minister bought a parrot
The congregation adored;
His name was Jeremiah
And he shouted, "Praise the Lord!"

He shouted it in the morning,
At noon and nighttime too;
And when the dear old bishop
Keeled over in the stew.

When the minister got an ulcer
He praised the Lord for that,
And when the poor man's underwear
Turned pink in the Laudromat.

"Praise the Lord!" he shouted out
When lightning struck the church;
He chuckled and screeched and praised the Lord
A-swingin' on his perch.

When the Reverend tripped on his surplice
Breaking his saintly leg,
You could hear that parrot praise the Lord
From here to Winnipeg.

Then something came over the minister,
A sort of un-Christian rage;
"Heavens!" shrieked Jeremiah
As he watched him approach the cage.

With a look that was most unholy,
You might even call it sinister,
As Jeremiah squawked his last,
"Praise the Lord," said the minister.

COBS

When we go to our cabin at the lake
My little brother sobs
Till we sweep down all the cobwebs...
He says he's afraid of the cobs.

IGUANODON

Iguanodon just stands around
Looking sort of sly;
Planning what he's going to do
As soon as his nail polish dries.

PTERODACTYL

She drifts through the night like a mythical kite
Over mountains and highways and streams;
The Great Pterodactyl is flying again
Since we asked her into our dreams.
She's come back to us here over millions of years
And she never will leave us again.
The Great Pterodactyl is flying once more,
Over oceans, and cities, and plains.

Part Two

Who Greased the Shoelaces?

RAIN, RAIN

Rain, rain, go away,
Come again another day...
Tomorrow Mom's in the marathon,
And the day after that the fair is on;
Tuesday the cousins are coming to play
(We drive Dad mad in the house all day);
Then we're doing a show in the yard that's funny
And rain makes the crêpe paper go all runny,
And then if it's good and everyone pays
We're going to do it some other days.
The week after that I'm going to camp,
I *hate* it at camp when everything's damp.
So rain, rain, go away,
Come back three weeks from Wednesday.

BUSY

I've walked in a walkathon,
Run in a marathon;
Swum in a swimathon,
Stared in a stare-a-thon.

Skipped in a skipathon,
Sung in a singathon;
Crawled in a crawlathon,

I'm crazy for thing-a-thons!!

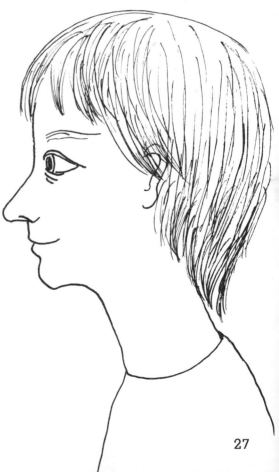

MURPHY #1

Suzy skipped across a stream,
Hopping on the rocks;
Suzy skipped across a stream
And hardly wet her socks.

Freddy jumped across a stream
In one mighty bound;
Freddy jumped across a stream
And landed on the ground.

Murphy bobbed across a stream
Floating in a tub;
Murphy bobbed across a stream...
Glub...
      Glub...
         Glub.

29

HOW TO TELL WHAT YOU'RE EATING

Apples snap between your teeth
With juicy, squirty zest;
Bananas loll upon your tongue,
All soggy and depressed.

A salad made of spinach leaves
Will make your tongue feel furry;
If fire glows from teeth to toes
You're likely eating curry.

If your face all shrivels up
The berry's goose or boysen,
And if your toes are pointing up
You'll know you've eaten poison.

A SLIVER OF LIVER

Just a sliver of liver they want me to eat,
It's good for my blood, they all say;
They want me to eat just the tiniest sliver
Of yukky old slimy old slithery liver;
I'm saying no thanks, not today.

No, I'll pass for tonight but tomorrow I might
Simply *beg* for a sliver of liver;
"Give me liver!" I'll cry. "I'll have liver or die!
Oh, *please* cook me a sliver of liver!"
One piece might not do, I'll need two or a few,
I'll want tons of the wobbly stuff,
Of that quivery shivery livery pile
There may not be nearly enough.

Just a sliver, you say? No thanks, not today.
Tomorrow, I really can't say;
But today I would sooner eat slivers of glass,
Eat the tail of a skunk washed down with gas,
Eat slivers of sidewalks and slivers of swings,
Slivers and slivers of any old thing,
Than a sliver of slimy old quivery shivery
Livery liver today.

MURPHY #2

Suzy caught a salmon
Swimming in a stream;
Suzy snagged a salmon
And cooked it up with cream.

Freddy found a flounder,
Mean and green and flat;
Freddy found a flounder
And fried it in some fat.

Murphy caught a minnow
And put it on to simmer;
Murphy got a minnow,
But no one came to dinner.

TODAY

Today I'm not going to hang around
Hoping you'll ask me to play
Hopscotch or marbles or ante-I-over,
I'm not going to do it today.

Today, I'll play where I darn well please,
Skip with my own darn skipping rope;
Today I'm not going to care a bit...
I hope. I hope. I hope.

WHO GREASED THE SHOELACES?

Every so often, I don't know why,
There's a day when your shoelaces won't stay tied;
Those are the days, it never fails,
When your hair won't stay in a ponytail,
In barrettes, or braids, or elastic ties,
Won't stay in a thing except your eyes.

And your blouse won't stay inside your pants,
And your socks fall down when you run or dance,
And your glasses slide to the end of your nose,
And you leave your jacket wherever you go.
It's always like that, I don't know why,
On the days when your shoelaces won't stay tied.

THESE SHOES

I love these shoes that once were white,
These old grub shoes Mom calls a sight,
With grass stains, grease stains, ink stains too,
And the hole in the toe where the dog has chewed.

They know just how to hug my feet,
So warm and snug and soft and neat;
When they're all worn out I'll sure be blue,
I'm just not *me* without these shoes.

RUNNING IN THE FAMILY

My father has taken up running for health,
He talks about nothing but that;
He's lean and he's mean and as brown as a bean,
He used to be funny and fat.

He talks about shinsplints and hamstrings and shoethings,
He's taking his pulse every minute;
He's going in a marathon over the mountains,
He actually thinks he will win it.

He runs on the lawn when he's mowing the grass;
He runs when he's setting the table;
He runs when he sweeps and he runs in his sleep;
I fear that my father's unstable.

Since my father has taken up running for health,
His belly is gone. And his beard.
He's as thin as a pin with only one chin,
But he's more than a little bit weird.

GRANDMA IS COMING!

Grandma is coming!
Grandma is coming!
She's coming tonight on the train;
So run and tell Barry
And Janie and Larry,
Grandma is coming again!

Grandma is coming,
She's lonesome for us,
Let's make a big sign for the door,
With words big and clear,
    !!! GRANDMA IS HERE !!!
Let's buy her a gift at the store.

Grandma is coming,
We hardly can wait,
Let's clean up our rooms and the yard;
We'll make her a cake
And a strawberry shake,
Let's all try to beat her at cards!

Grandma is coming,
That's always the best,
We can show her those beautiful stones,
And the playhouse and swings,
And tell her things...
She'll never believe how we've grown!

Grandma is coming!
Grandma is coming!
The train is arriving at ten:
We'll all go to meet her,
Oh, what could be sweeter?
Grandma is coming again!

MURPHY #3

Suzy rode a skateboard,
Whizzing down the street;
Doing ollie-kick-flips
And looking really neat.

Freddy rode a skateboard
And did an ollie-shove-it;
He did it in a half pipe
And everybody loved it.

Murphy rode a skateboard
And tried a plain old ollie;
Murphy didn't do it right,
He doesn't feel too jolly.

SNOW

Snowflakes falling silently
Like ragged bits of lace;
Tiny cool fairy kisses
On my upturned face.

ANGELS

I'm making angels here in the snow;
The temperature's minus twenty-seven;
If I don't stop doing it pretty darn soon
I'll be flapping my wings in heaven.

FACE-OFF

I got a fat lip last Saturday night
When the goal post said hi to my head;
Then a stick got stuck in the blade of my skate
And I turned the blueline red.

I flattened my nose up against the boards;
I'm thinking it must be a sign
Not to forget my helmet again,
Or the *face off* is going to be mine!

MURPHY #4

Suzy walked a tightrope,
High up in the air;
Suzy walked a tightrope,
And wasn't even scared.

Freddy walked a tightrope,
Looking debonair;
Freddy walked a tightrope
Balancing a bear.

Murphy walked a tightrope,
Full of fear and trembling;
Murphy walked a tightrope,
Murphy's re-assembling.

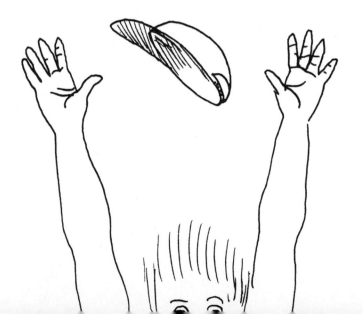

METAMORPHOSIS

Your parka's gone, and your boots and scarf,
And your toque's gone too, and there you are;
Your hair is there and your arms are bare,
And your last year's shorts are barely there;
You look so white and you feel so light
Like maybe you shed a cocoon last night;
Your neck feels naked, and your feet look funny,
Your nose does too, and it's also runny;
It's always in spring that you see these things,
Somehow you kind of *stick out* in the spring.

EARS

Some are big and some are small;
Some are wide and wary;
Some are neat and some are sweet,
And some are sort of hairy.

SPRINKLE SPRINKLE

Sprinkle sprinkle little tar
On my father's brand-new car;
Sprinkle language impolite
In the dark and tarry night.

ALLERGIC

My pillow's full of feathers
So they've taken it away;
My cat is full of cat hair
So they put him out to stay;
The comforter that comforts me
Got thrown out with the cat;
They took my Snoopy curtains
And they even took the mat.
My hives are gone, my itches too,
I never even sneeze,
Now my skin is only covered
With a little bit of breeze.

I'm frozen and I'm lonesome
And I'm oh, so depressed,
In my cold little hard little bed;
But my cat doesn't care,
He's covered with hair,
And all of the rest of my bed!

TWO'S COMPANY

Two's company, three's a crowd,
I heard that from my mother;
Did you say it today as you walked away
With your arms around each other?

You've been so mean that I shouldn't care,
Your *awfulness* should comfort me...
But oh, just then, as you walked away,
I'd have given most anything today,
To be half of the company.

MURPHY #5

Suzy saw a lion
Sittin' in a zoo;
Suzy saw a lion
And let it lick her shoe.

Freddy saw a lion
In an animal parade;
Freddy saw a lion
And gave it lemonade.

Murphy saw a lion
Lyin' on the plain;
Murphy saw a lion
But he won't see one again.

BONNIE

Bonnie likes me,
Bonnie doesn't,
Bonnie doesn't know;
She'll play with me,
And then she won't,
And that's the way it goes.

It used to really bother me
But now it's only boring;
Bonnie, do you hear that sound?
Excuse me, but I'm snoring.

THONGS

I want to wear thongs like the rest of the throng,
Like my friend and my brother and sister;
They all look so cool,
I just look like a fool,
Limping along with a blister.

They all skim around with their soles on the ground
And the tops of their feet nice and airy,
While I hobble behind
With my feet on my mind
And a pain in my toe that is scary.

There's a crick in my neck from looking down,
There are hideous pains in my feet;
There's everything wrong
When *I* try to wear thongs,
But darn it, they look so neat!

ADVICE

When your dad is mad and your mother too,
And the whole darn world is mad at you;

And your mom and dad are mad at each other,
And it's not your fault, it's all your brother's;

And the sun won't shine and the rain won't fall
And it's cold and stupid outside is all;

And your friend didn't write you a single letter,
And you doubt if tomorrow will be any better;

What do you do? And how do you do it?
Don't ask me. I just get through it.

LONELY

I miss my bed when I'm at camp,
I *dream* about it when everything's damp;
At home it doesn't rain on my head,
Well, it does, but not when I'm in my bed.

I miss my friend and my dog and cat,
I even miss my brother (the rat);
But when everything's lumpy and cold and damp,
It's my bed I miss the most at camp.

MURPHY #6

Suzy ate a mushroom
Stewing in a stew;
Suzy ate a mushroom
And said, "What's new?"

Freddy ate a mushroom,
Frying in a pan;
Freddy ate a mushroom
And grew up to be a man.

Murphy ate a mushroom
Growing on the lawn;
Murphy ate a mushroom...

CHANGING YOUR MIND

"Would you like to change your mind?" they say
(This person, and that, and the other one);
And I always think I would if I could
'Cause the one I have is not very good,
But they never say how to *do* it,

Or where to go get another one.

JIMMY LORRIS

A quiet little genius,
Whose name was Jimmy Lorris,
Was hooked on reading everything,
But mostly his thesaurus.
He read it through and through and through,
All of his own volition;
Committed it to memory too,
The new enlarged edition.

Now every time he opens up
His mouth he gets in trouble;
Synonyms keep floating out
Like someone blowing bubbles.
At first this really pleased his folks,
Appealing to their vanity;
Then they said if he didn't stop
He'd drive them to insanity.

Father said at dinnertime
He was feeling rather low,
His income down, inflation up,
And business somewhat slow.
"Poor Dad," said Jim, "business is tardy,
Sluggish, humdrum, gradual, slack,
Languid, leaden, passive, backward — "
His mom gave him a smack.

"Jimmy," implored his father,
Don't *do* that all the time.
Mommy's getting nervous,
She's no longer in her prime."
"Is Mom nervous, timid, irritable,
Hysterical, shaky, aghast,
Apprehensive, restless, shocked,
A nervous wreck at last?"

His mother screamed and tore her hair
And wrung her hands and feet;
"Shut up!" she yelled, "you rotten kid,
You yappy little creep!"
With his hand upon his Roget
A solemn oath Jim swore:
"Not one synonym will cross my lips,
Not one, no, nevermore.

"Are you happy, gratified, satisfied,
Gladdened, delighted, cheered?"
His mom leapt over the table,
And the look in her eyes was weird.
As she led little Jimmy out in the yard
Father heard her say...
"Kill. Butcher. Slaughter. Dispatch.
Assassinate. Massacre. Slay."

GET YOUR NOSE OUT OF THAT BOOK

"You've always got your nose in a book!"
That's what people say;
And it's true, I suppose, about my nose
But I just can't take it away.
If I live to be a hundred and three
I'll never get finished, for can't they see
That even as I'm speeding through one,
Somebody's busy writing a new one.